DYSPHAGIA COOKBOOK

FOR BEGINNERS

A Three-Phase Guide to Soft Food Diet Recipes, Meal
Planning, and Preparation for the Newly Diagnosed"

Amos jimmy

TABLE OF CONTENT

INTRODUCTION

Embarking on a culinary journey with dysphagia can seem daunting at first glance. The quest for meals that are both safe and enjoyable may feel limiting, yet this challenge also opens the door to a world of creativity, flavor, and nutrition. "Dysphagia Cookbook for Beginners" is designed to be your companion through this journey, offering a beacon of hope and a collection of recipes that prove a diagnosis does not define the boundaries of delicious and satisfying eating.

In these pages, you'll discover not just recipes, but a new way of thinking about food and meal preparation. We'll explore the fundamentals of dysphagia-friendly cooking, from understanding the levels of food texture to mastering the art of flavor enhancement, ensuring that every dish brings joy and nourishment. Whether you're cooking for yourself or a loved one, these recipes are crafted to meet nutritional needs without compromising taste.

This cookbook is a beginner's guide, which means we start with the basics and progressively guide you through the intricacies of dysphagia-friendly cooking. It's filled with tips, techniques, and adaptations to traditional meals, alongside entirely novel dishes—all of which are designed to cater to varying levels of dysphagia and personal preferences.

CHAPTER 1

UNDERSTANDING DYSPHAGIA

Before delving into the specifics of the dysphagia diet, it's crucial to understand what dysphagia is. Dysphagia is not a disease in itself but a symptom stemming from various causes, including neurological conditions, certain cancers, and physical obstructions or muscle weaknesses in the throat and esophagus. Recognizing the signs of dysphagia, such as coughing or choking during meals, a sensation of food being stuck in the throat, or recurrent pneumonia, is the first step toward appropriate management.

The Role of a Dysphagia Diet

The primary goal of a dysphagia diet is to minimize the risk of food or liquid entering the lungs, which can lead to pneumonia, and to ensure that nutritional needs are met. This is achieved by modifying the texture of foods and the thickness of liquids to make them safer and easier to swallow. A well-structured dysphagia diet balances safety, nutrition, and enjoyment of food, crucial for maintaining quality of life.

Texture Modifications: The Levels of a Dysphagia Diet

Dysphagia diets are categorized into levels based on the texture of foods and thickness of liquids. Understanding and implementing these levels is paramount for a safe swallowing experience.

Level 1: Pureed (Very Thick)

Foods: Smooth, cohesive, and pudding-like, requiring no chewing. Examples include pureed fruits, vegetables, and meats, as well as smooth porridges and soups.

Liquids: May include thickened beverages to a pudding-like consistency.

Level 2: Mechanically Altered (Soft)

Foods: Moist, soft foods that require some chewing but are easier to swallow than regular foods. Examples are soft-boiled vegetables, finely ground or minced meats, and soft, ripe fruits.

Liquids: Thicker than water but less thick than Level 1 liquids, often compared to a nectar-like consistency.

Level 3: Advanced (Soft with Caution)

Foods: Foods are near-normal but avoid hard, sticky, or crunchy items. Well-cooked vegetables, tender meats, and soft, non-crusty bread are suitable.

Liquids: Generally, all drinkable liquids that are easier to swallow and control.

Each level caters to different severities of dysphagia, and moving between levels should always be done under the guidance of healthcare professionals, such as a speech-language pathologist or a dietitian specialized in dysphagia.

Step-by-Step Guide to Implementing a Dysphagia Diet

Step 1: Assessment by a Healthcare Professional

The journey begins with a thorough assessment by a healthcare professional to determine the severity of dysphagia and the most appropriate diet level.

Step 2: Understanding Suitable Foods and Textures

Familiarize yourself with the foods and textures that correspond to the recommended diet level. Experiment with recipes and food options to maintain nutritional balance and variety.

Step 3: Meal Preparation and Safety

Prepare meals according to the guidelines of the recommended diet level, paying close attention to texture and consistency. Ensure food is evenly textured and free of lumps or hard pieces that could pose a risk.

Step 4: Eating and Monitoring

Eat slowly, taking small bites and sips, and remain upright during and after eating to facilitate safer swallowing. Monitor for any signs of difficulty or discomfort, and adjust the diet as necessary under professional guidance.

Step 5: Regular Review and Adjustment

Dysphagia can change over time, necessitating regular reassessment and potential adjustments to the diet. Stay in close contact with your healthcare team to ensure the diet remains appropriate for your needs.

CHAPTER 2

BREAKFAST RECIPES LEVEL 1: PUREED (VERY THICK)

Pureed Butternut Squash Soup

Serves: 1

Cooking Time: 25 minutes

Ingredients and Portions/Measurements:

- Butternut Squash (pureed dysphagia diet friendly): 1 cup cooked and pureed
- Low-Sodium Vegetable Broth (pureed dysphagia diet friendly): 1 cup
- Olive Oil: 1 teaspoon
- Ground Cinnamon: 1/4 teaspoon
- Nutmeg: A pinch
- Salt (tolerated by few patients): Substitute with a pinch of salt substitute if necessary

Instructions:

- In a medium saucepan, heat the olive oil over medium heat.
- Add the pureed butternut squash to the pan and stir to combine with the olive oil.
- Gradually add the low-sodium vegetable broth to the pan, stirring constantly to ensure a smooth consistency.
- Add the ground cinnamon and nutmeg to the soup, and stir well.
- Bring the soup to a simmer, then reduce the heat to low and cook for 20 minutes, stirring occasionally.
- If necessary, use a blender to puree the soup further until it reaches a smooth, velvety texture suitable for a Level 1 dysphagia diet.
- Taste the soup and adjust seasoning with a pinch of salt substitute if needed.
- Serve warm.

Scientific Notes:

- Butternut Squash: High in vitamins A and C, butternut squash is a nutritious choice for those on a dysphagia diet. Vitamin A supports eye health and immune function, while vitamin C is crucial for skin health and iron absorption. The smooth texture of pureed butternut squash is ideal for a Level 1 dysphagia diet, ensuring safe swallowing.

- Low-Sodium Vegetable Broth: Using low-sodium vegetable broth helps manage blood pressure and is essential for those with dietary restrictions related to sodium intake. It also adds necessary fluids to the diet, aiding in hydration.

- Olive Oil: A source of monounsaturated fats, olive oil is beneficial for heart health. It also helps create a smoother texture in purees, making them easier to swallow for individuals with dysphagia.

- Spices (Cinnamon & Nutmeg): Spices add flavor without posing a risk to those with swallowing difficulties. Cinnamon can help regulate blood sugar levels, while nutmeg has been shown to have anti-inflammatory properties.

- Salt Substitute: For those who cannot tolerate sodium, a salt substitute can be used to season the soup without increasing the risk of hypertension or heart disease.

Nutritional Information (per serving):

- Calories: Approximately 150

- Protein: 2g
- Total Fat: 5g
- Saturated Fat: Less than 1g
- Carbohydrates: 27g
- Fiber: 5g
- Sodium: Less than 100mg (varies with the use of salt substitute)

Smooth Carrot and Ginger Puree

Serves: 1

Cooking Time: 30 minutes

Ingredients and Portions/Measurements:

- Carrots (pureed dysphagia diet friendly): 2 large carrots, peeled and chopped
- Ginger (tolerated by few patients): 1 teaspoon, grated (Substitution: pinch of ginger powder)
- Olive Oil (pureed dysphagia diet friendly): 1 tablespoon
- Low-Sodium Chicken or Vegetable Broth (pureed dysphagia diet friendly): 1 cup
- Salt (tolerated by few patients): A pinch (Substitution: Salt substitute)

Instructions:

- In a medium pot, heat the olive oil over medium heat. Add the chopped carrots and cook until they start to soften, about 5 minutes.
- Add the grated ginger (or ginger powder) to the pot and cook for another 1-2 minutes, until fragrant.

- Pour in the low-sodium chicken or vegetable broth and bring to a boil. Reduce heat and simmer until the carrots are very tender, about 20 minutes.
- Once the carrots are tender, use a blender or an immersion blender to puree the mixture until smooth. If the puree is too thick, add a little more broth to reach the desired consistency.
- Season with a pinch of salt or salt substitute to taste.
- Serve warm, ensuring the puree is smooth and free of lumps for easy swallowing.

Scientific Notes:

- Carrots: Rich in beta-carotene, which the body converts into vitamin A, essential for good vision, immune function, and skin health. The soft texture of cooked and pureed carrots is ideal for a Level 1 dysphagia diet.
- Ginger: Known for its anti-inflammatory properties and potential to aid digestion. However, fresh ginger may not be tolerated by all patients due to its strong flavor; a ginger powder substitute can offer flavor without the intensity.
- Olive Oil: A source of healthy monounsaturated fats, olive oil can help ensure the puree has a smooth

consistency, making swallowing easier. It's also known for its anti-inflammatory effects and benefits to heart health.

- Low-Sodium Broth: Provides hydration and flavor without the risk of contributing to hypertension. Using a low-sodium option is important for managing salt intake, particularly in individuals with dietary restrictions.

- Salt/Salt Substitute: While salt enhances flavor, it should be used sparingly, especially in diets where sodium intake needs to be monitored. A salt substitute can offer a safer alternative for those with high blood pressure or heart conditions.

Nutritional Information (per serving):

- Calories: Approximately 140
- Protein: 2g
- Total Fat: 7g
- Saturated Fat: 1g
- Carbohydrates: 19g
- Fiber: 5g
- Sodium: Varies with the use of salt or salt substitute

Creamy Avocado and Spinach Puree

Serves: 1

Cooking Time: 10 minutes

Ingredients and Portions/Measurements:

- Avocado (pureed dysphagia diet friendly): 1/2 ripe avocado
- Spinach (pureed dysphagia diet friendly): 1/2 cup cooked and cooled
- Olive Oil: 1 teaspoon
- Lemon Juice (tolerated by few patients): 1 teaspoon (Substitution: a pinch of citric acid for a similar tangy flavor)
- Salt: A pinch (Substitution: Salt substitute)

Instructions:

- In a blender, combine the ripe avocado and cooked spinach.
- Add olive oil to help achieve a smooth, creamy texture.
- Blend on high until the mixture is completely smooth, with no lumps or pieces, ensuring it's suitable for a Level 1 dysphagia diet.

- Add lemon juice or a pinch of citric acid and blend again to mix thoroughly.
- Season with a pinch of salt or salt substitute to taste.
- Serve immediately, ensuring the puree is at a safe, comfortable temperature for consumption.

Scientific Notes:

- Avocado: High in monounsaturated fats, avocados are beneficial for heart health and provide a creamy texture that's ideal for pureed diets. They're also a good source of fiber, potassium, and vitamins C, E, and K.
- Spinach: Spinach is rich in iron, calcium, and vitamins A, C, and K1. It's also high in antioxidants and can contribute to a healthy diet, especially when pureed for easy swallowing.
- Olive Oil: Adds healthy fats to the diet and helps create a smoother puree, facilitating easier swallowing for individuals with dysphagia.
- Lemon Juice/Citric Acid: Both add a bright, acidic flavor to the puree. Citric acid can be a gentler option for those who find lemon juice too harsh or acidic.

- Salt/Salt Substitute: Used to enhance the flavor of the puree. Salt substitutes can provide a safer option for individuals needing to manage their sodium intake.

Nutritional Information (per serving):

- Calories: Approximately 200
- Protein: 3g
- Total Fat: 17g (mostly monounsaturated)
- Saturated Fat: 2.5g
- Carbohydrates: 12g
- Fiber: 7g
- Sodium: Varies with the use of salt or salt substitute

Silky Pear Puree

Serves: 1

Cooking Time: 5 minutes

Ingredients and Portions/Measurements:

- Pear (pureed dysphagia diet friendly): 1 large ripe pear, peeled and cored
- Cinnamon (pureed dysphagia diet friendly): 1/4 teaspoon
- Vanilla Extract (tolerated by few patients): 1/4 teaspoon (Substitution: a pinch of vanilla powder)
- Honey (tolerated by few patients): 1 teaspoon (Substitution: Maple syrup)

Instructions:

- Place the peeled and cored pear in a blender.
- Add cinnamon and vanilla extract (or vanilla powder) to the blender.
- Blend until the mixture is completely smooth, checking to ensure no lumps remain.
- Taste and adjust sweetness with honey or maple syrup if desired. Blend again to incorporate.

- Serve the puree at room temperature or slightly chilled, ensuring it's safe and comfortable to swallow.

Scientific Notes:

- Pear: Pears are a good source of dietary fiber, vitamin C, and several antioxidants. They provide a naturally sweet flavor and smooth texture when pureed, suitable for a Level 1 dysphagia diet.
- Cinnamon: Offers anti-inflammatory properties and can help regulate blood sugar levels. Its fine powder form blends seamlessly into purees.
- Vanilla Extract/Vanilla Powder: Both add flavor depth to the puree. Vanilla powder can be a suitable substitute for those sensitive to alcohol in extracts.
- Honey/Maple Syrup: Natural sweeteners that can enhance the flavor of the puree. Maple syrup is a vegan alternative to honey and offers minerals like manganese and zinc.

Nutritional Information (per serving):

- Calories: Approximately 120
- Protein: 0.5g
- Total Fat: 0g
- Saturated Fat: 0g

- Carbohydrates: 31g
- Fiber: 5g
- Sodium: 0mg

Blueberry Banana Smoothie Puree

Serves: 1

Cooking Time: 5 minutes

Ingredients and Portions/Measurements:

- Banana (pureed dysphagia diet friendly): 1 ripe banana
- Blueberries (pureed dysphagia diet friendly): 1/2 cup
- Greek Yogurt (tolerated by few patients): 1/2 cup (Substitution: lactose-free yogurt)
- Honey (tolerated by few patients): 1 tablespoon (Substitution: maple syrup)
- Ice Cubes (optional, for texture): 4-5 cubes

Instructions:

- Place the ripe banana, blueberries, Greek yogurt (or its substitution), and honey (or maple syrup) in a blender.
- Add ice cubes if a colder texture is desired.

- Blend until the mixture is completely smooth, with no chunks or seeds, ensuring it's suitable for a Level 1 dysphagia diet.
- Pour the smoothie puree into a glass and serve immediately.

Scientific Notes:

- Banana and Blueberries: Both are excellent sources of dietary fiber, vitamins, and antioxidants. Bananas provide potassium, which is crucial for heart health and muscle function. Blueberries are known for their high antioxidant levels, which can protect the body from oxidative stress.
- Greek Yogurt: A good source of protein and probiotics. Probiotics are beneficial for gut health. If lactose intolerant, lactose-free yogurt can be used as an alternative, providing similar nutritional benefits without the lactose, which can be difficult for some people to digest.
- Honey/Maple Syrup: Natural sweeteners to enhance flavor. Maple syrup is a vegan-friendly option and contains minerals like manganese and zinc.

Nutritional Information (per serving):

- Calories: Approximately 250
- Protein: 10g
- Total Fat: 1g
- Saturated Fat: 0.5g
- Carbohydrates: 55g
- Fiber: 4g
- Sodium: 50mg

LUNCH RECIPES LEVEL 1: PUREED (VERY THICK)

Creamy Potato and Leek Soup Puree

Serves: 1

Cooking Time: 30 minutes

Ingredients and Portions/Measurements:

- Potatoes (pureed dysphagia diet friendly): 2 medium potatoes, peeled and cubed
- Leek (pureed dysphagia diet friendly): 1 leek, white and light green parts only, cleaned and sliced
- Low-Sodium Vegetable Broth (pureed dysphagia diet friendly): 2 cups
- Olive Oil: 1 tablespoon
- Ground Nutmeg: 1/4 teaspoon
- Salt: A pinch (Substitution: Salt substitute)

Instructions:

- In a pot, heat the olive oil over medium heat. Add the sliced leeks and cook until soft, about 5 minutes.
- Add the cubed potatoes and cover with low-sodium vegetable broth. Bring to a boil, then reduce heat and

simmer until the potatoes are tender, about 20 minutes.

- Once the vegetables are soft, use an immersion blender or standard blender to puree the soup until smooth.
- Add the ground nutmeg and blend again. Season with a pinch of salt or salt substitute to taste.
- Serve warm, ensuring the soup's texture is suitable for a Level 1 dysphagia diet.

Scientific Notes:

- Potatoes: A good source of carbohydrates, providing energy, and vitamins, such as vitamin C, which supports the immune system. Their soft texture when cooked and pureed is perfect for a dysphagia diet.
- Leek: Leeks are high in vitamins A, C, and K, as well as dietary fiber. They add flavor and nutritional value to the soup.
- Olive Oil: Contains monounsaturated fats, beneficial for heart health. It also helps create a smoother consistency in the puree.
- Nutmeg: Adds flavor and has been associated with digestive health benefits.

Nutritional Information (per serving):

- Calories: Approximately 300
- Protein: 4g
- Total Fat: 7g
- Saturated Fat: 1g
- Carbohydrates: 54g
- Fiber: 6g
- Sodium: 100mg

Smooth Pumpkin Puree

Serves: 1

Cooking Time: 20 minutes

Ingredients and Portions/Measurements:

- Pumpkin (pureed dysphagia diet friendly): 1 cup cooked and pureed
- Olive Oil: 1 teaspoon (For cooking, adds healthy fats)
- Ground Cinnamon: 1/4 teaspoon (Adds flavor, pureed dysphagia diet friendly)
- Ground Ginger: A pinch (Tolerated by few patients; Substitution: A pinch of ginger powder for a milder taste)
- Maple Syrup: 1 tablespoon (Adds sweetness, tolerated by few patients; Substitution: Honey for those not sensitive to it)

Instructions:

- Preheat your oven to 350°F (175°C). Slice the pumpkin into chunks, remove seeds, and brush lightly with olive oil.
- Roast the pumpkin chunks until tender, about 15-20 minutes.

- Once cooled, scoop the pumpkin flesh into a blender. Add a bit of water if needed to facilitate blending.
- Add cinnamon, ginger (or ginger powder), and maple syrup (or honey). Blend until the mixture is completely smooth.
- Serve immediately, ensuring the puree is at a comfortable temperature for consumption.

Scientific Notes:

- Pumpkin: High in vitamins A and C, fiber, and antioxidants. Vitamin A supports vision and immune function, while vitamin C aids in skin health and iron absorption.
- Olive Oil: Contains monounsaturated fats, beneficial for heart health.
- Cinnamon and Ginger: Both spices are known for their anti-inflammatory properties and can aid digestion.
- Maple Syrup/Honey: Natural sweeteners; maple syrup provides minerals like manganese.

Nutritional Information (per serving):

- Calories: Approximately 180
- Protein: 2g

- Total Fat: 4g
- Saturated Fat: 0.5g
- Carbohydrates: 37g
- Fiber: 3g
- Sodium: 5mg

Silken Tofu and Berry Puree

Serves: 1

Cooking Time: 10 minutes

Ingredients and Portions/Measurements:

- Silken Tofu (pureed dysphagia diet friendly): 1/2 cup
- Mixed Berries (pureed dysphagia diet friendly): 1/2 cup (fresh or frozen)
- Honey: 1 teaspoon (Tolerated by few patients; Substitution: Maple syrup for those with honey sensitivities)
- Lemon Juice: A few drops (Adds brightness, tolerated by few patients; Substitution: A pinch of citric acid for a similar effect)

Instructions:

- Place silken tofu, mixed berries, honey (or maple syrup), and a few drops of lemon juice (or a pinch of citric acid) in a blender.
- Blend until completely smooth, with no chunks or seeds, ensuring it's appropriate for a Level 1 dysphagia diet.

- Taste and adjust the sweetness if necessary by adding a little more honey or maple syrup.
- Serve the puree chilled or at room temperature, as preferred.

Scientific Notes:

- Silken Tofu: A great source of protein and a smooth texture suitable for dysphagia diets. It contains soy isoflavones, which have been linked to improved heart health.
- Mixed Berries: High in antioxidants, vitamins, and fiber. Berries can contribute to overall health, including heart health and inflammation reduction.
- Honey/Maple Syrup: Both add sweetness naturally. Maple syrup is a suitable vegan alternative and contains several minerals.
- Lemon Juice/Citric Acid: Adds a fresh flavor and can enhance the taste of the puree. Citric acid is a more controlled way to add acidity without altering texture.

Nutritional Information (per serving):

- Calories: Approximately 150
- Protein: 8g
- Total Fat: 4g

- Saturated Fat: 0.5g
- Carbohydrates: 22g
- Fiber: 3g
- Sodium: 15mg

Pear and Avocado Puree

Serves: 1

Cooking Time: 10 minutes

Ingredients and Portions/Measurements:

- Pear (pureed dysphagia diet friendly): 1 medium pear, peeled and cored
- Avocado (pureed dysphagia diet friendly): 1/2 medium avocado
- Lemon Juice (tolerated by few patients): 1 teaspoon (Substitution: A pinch of citric acid for a similar tangy effect)
- Honey (tolerated by few patients): 1 teaspoon (Substitution: Agave syrup)

Instructions:

- Blend the peeled and cored pear and the avocado in a blender until smooth.

- Add lemon juice (or citric acid) to prevent browning and add a bit of zest.
- Sweeten with honey or agave syrup as preferred and blend again until all ingredients are well combined.
- Serve immediately, ensuring the texture is smooth and without lumps, perfect for a Level 1 dysphagia diet.

Scientific Notes:

- Pear and Avocado: Both are high in fiber and provide a smooth consistency when blended, ideal for those on a dysphagia diet. Pears offer vitamins C and K, while avocados are rich in healthy fats, vitamins E, C, and K, and folate.
- Lemon Juice/Citric Acid: Helps to preserve the color of the puree and adds a refreshing taste. Citric acid is a less allergenic substitute for those sensitive to citrus.
- Honey/Agave Syrup: Both are natural sweeteners; agave syrup is a fructose-based sweetener that's a vegan-friendly option.

Nutritional Information (per serving):

- Calories: Approximately 250
- Protein: 2g

- Total Fat: 15g
- Saturated Fat: 2g
- Carbohydrates: 30g
- Fiber: 7g
- Sodium: 10mg

Creamy Broccoli and Potato Puree

Serves: 1

Cooking Time: 25 minutes

Ingredients and Portions/Measurements:

- Potato (pureed dysphagia diet friendly): 1 large potato, peeled
- Broccoli (pureed dysphagia diet friendly): 1 cup of florets
- Olive Oil: 1 tablespoon
- Garlic Powder (tolerated by few patients): 1/4 teaspoon (Substitution: A pinch of asafoetida for a similar flavor without the irritants)
- Salt: A pinch (Substitution: Potassium chloride for those on a sodium-restricted diet)

Instructions:

- Boil the potato until tender, then drain.

- Steam the broccoli florets until very soft.
- In a blender, combine the potato, broccoli, olive oil, and seasonings. Add a bit of water if needed for blending.
- Blend until the mixture is completely smooth, suitable for Level 1 dysphagia diet.
- Adjust the seasoning to taste, using the appropriate substitutions as needed.
- Serve warm, ensuring the puree is easily swallowable.

Scientific Notes:

- Potato and Broccoli: Potatoes provide carbohydrates and potassium, while broccoli offers dietary fiber, vitamin C, and vitamin K. Both are excellent for creating a nutrient-rich puree that's easy to swallow.
- Olive Oil: Adds healthy fats to the diet and improves the texture of the puree.
- Garlic Powder/Asafoetida: Both add flavor without adding bulk. Asafoetida is a good substitute for those who might have difficulty digesting garlic.
- Salt/Potassium Chloride: Potassium chloride is a salt substitute that can help manage potassium levels for those on a sodium-restricted diet.

Nutritional Information (per serving):

- Calories: Approximately 200
- Protein: 4g
- Total Fat: 14g
- Saturated Fat: 2g
- Carbohydrates: 20g
- Fiber: 5g
- Sodium: 20mg (varies with substitutions)

DINNER RECIPES LEVEL 1: PUREED (VERY THICK)

Silky Mango and Coconut Puree

Serves: 1

Cooking Time: 5 minutes

Ingredients and Portions/Measurements:

- Mango (pureed dysphagia diet friendly): 1 large ripe mango, peeled and stone removed
- Coconut Milk (pureed dysphagia diet friendly): 1/4 cup
- Honey (tolerated by few patients): 1 teaspoon (Substitution: Agave nectar for those with honey sensitivities)
- Lime Juice: A few drops (tolerated by few patients; Substitution: A pinch of citric acid for those sensitive to citrus)

Instructions:

- Combine the ripe mango and coconut milk in a blender.
- Add honey or agave nectar to sweeten.

- Add a few drops of lime juice or a pinch of citric acid to enhance the flavor.
- Blend until completely smooth, with no lumps, ensuring suitability for a Level 1 dysphagia diet.
- Serve immediately, ensuring the puree is at a comfortable temperature for consumption.

Scientific Notes:

- Mango: High in vitamin C, vitamin A, and fiber, mangoes can support immune function and eye health. Their natural sweetness and creamy texture when blended make them ideal for pureed diets.
- Coconut Milk: Provides healthy fats, which are important for energy and supporting cell growth. It also adds creaminess to the puree, making it easier to swallow.
- Honey/Agave Nectar: Both are natural sweeteners; agave nectar is a low glycemic index option, making it a suitable substitute for honey.
- Lime Juice/Citric Acid: Adds a refreshing taste. Citric acid can be used as a substitute to avoid the allergenic potential of lime juice.

Nutritional Information (per serving):

- Calories: Approximately 200
- Protein: 2g
- Total Fat: 5g
- Saturated Fat: 4g
- Carbohydrates: 40g
- Fiber: 3g
- Sodium: 5mg

Velvety Sweet Potato and Carrot Puree

Serves: 1

Cooking Time: 30 minutes

Ingredients and Portions/Measurements:

- Sweet Potato (pureed dysphagia diet friendly): 1 medium sweet potato, peeled
- Carrot (pureed dysphagia diet friendly): 2 medium carrots, peeled
- Olive Oil: 1 tablespoon
- Ground Cinnamon: 1/4 teaspoon (pureed dysphagia diet friendly)
- Nutmeg: A pinch (tolerated by few patients; Substitution: A pinch of allspice for a similar flavor profile)

Instructions:

- Boil or steam the sweet potato and carrots until very tender.
- Transfer the cooked vegetables to a blender. Add olive oil for smoothness.
- Add ground cinnamon and a pinch of nutmeg or allspice.

- Blend until the mixture achieves a smooth, velvety consistency suitable for Level 1 dysphagia diets.
- Adjust the seasoning to taste, then serve warm, ensuring the puree is easy to swallow.

Scientific Notes:

- Sweet Potato: Rich in beta-carotene (converted to vitamin A in the body), fiber, and vitamins C and B6. Supports vision, immune function, and gut health.
- Carrot: High in beta-carotene, fiber, and vitamin K1. Supports eye health and provides antioxidants.
- Olive Oil: Adds healthy monounsaturated fats and helps create a smoother consistency in the puree.
- Cinnamon and Nutmeg/Allspice: Adds warmth and depth to the flavor. Both spices offer anti-inflammatory properties and aid in digestion.

Nutritional Information (per serving):

- Calories: Approximately 250
- Protein: 3g
- Total Fat: 7g
- Saturated Fat: 1g
- Carbohydrates: 45g
- Fiber: 7g

- Sodium: 80mg

Creamed Spinach and White Bean Puree

Serves: 1

Cooking Time: 20 minutes

Ingredients and Portions/Measurements:

- Cooked White Beans (pureed dysphagia diet friendly): 1/2 cup
- Spinach (pureed dysphagia diet friendly): 1 cup fresh or frozen
- Olive Oil: 1 tablespoon
- Garlic Powder: 1/4 teaspoon (Substitution: A pinch of asafoetida for those with garlic sensitivities)
- Nutritional Yeast (optional, for a cheesy flavor): 1 tablespoon (pureed dysphagia diet friendly)

Instructions:

- If using fresh spinach, steam until wilted and soft. If using frozen, thaw and drain well.
- In a blender, combine the cooked white beans, spinach, olive oil, garlic powder (or asafoetida), and nutritional yeast if using.

- Blend until the mixture is completely smooth, with no lumps or fibers, ensuring it's suitable for a Level 1 dysphagia diet.
- Taste and adjust the seasoning as needed. The puree should be creamy and smooth.
- Serve warm, ensuring the texture is consistent for easy swallowing.

Scientific Notes:

- White Beans: A great source of protein and fiber, aiding in digestion and muscle repair.
- Spinach: Rich in vitamins A, C, and K, as well as iron and calcium, supporting bone health and the immune system.
- Olive Oil: Provides healthy fats for heart health and aids in achieving a smooth puree texture.
- Nutritional Yeast: Adds a cheese-like flavor and is a source of B vitamins, including B12, which is essential for nerve function and energy production.

Nutritional Information (per serving):

- Calories: Approximately 220
- Protein: 10g
- Total Fat: 9g

- Saturated Fat: 1.5g
- Carbohydrates: 27g
- Fiber: 8g
- Sodium: 20mg (may vary with substitutions)

Butternut Squash and Apple Puree

Serves: 1

Cooking Time: 25 minutes

Ingredients and Portions/Measurements:

- Butternut Squash (pureed dysphagia diet friendly): 1 cup, peeled and cubed
- Apple (pureed dysphagia diet friendly): 1 medium, peeled and cored
- Cinnamon: 1/4 teaspoon (pureed dysphagia diet friendly)
- Ground Ginger: A pinch (tolerated by few patients; Substitution: A pinch of ground cardamom for a different flavor profile)
- Water or Apple Juice: As needed for blending

Instructions:

- Steam the butternut squash and apple until they are very tender.

- Transfer the cooked squash and apple to a blender. Add cinnamon, ginger (or cardamom), and a little water or apple juice to facilitate blending.
- Blend until completely smooth, with no chunks or fibrous material, suitable for a Level 1 dysphagia diet.
- Adjust the consistency if needed by adding more liquid, blending to a perfectly smooth puree.
- Serve warm or chilled, according to preference, ensuring it's easy to swallow.

Scientific Notes:

- Butternut Squash: High in vitamins A and C, offering immune support and antioxidant benefits.
- Apple: Provides fiber and vitamin C. The natural sweetness of apples complements the squash well.
- Cinnamon and Ginger/Cardamom: These spices add flavor complexity and have anti-inflammatory properties.

Nutritional Information (per serving):

- Calories: Approximately 150
- Protein: 2g
- Total Fat: 0.5g
- Saturated Fat: 0g

- Carbohydrates: 38g
- Fiber: 6g
- Sodium: 10mg

Cauliflower and Turmeric Puree

Serves: 1

Cooking Time: 20 minutes

Ingredients and Portions/Measurements:

- Cauliflower (pureed dysphagia diet friendly): 1 cup florets
- Turmeric Powder: 1/2 teaspoon (pureed dysphagia diet friendly)
- Olive Oil: 1 tablespoon
- Low-Sodium Vegetable Broth: 1/2 cup (Substitution: Water for those needing a lower sodium option)
- Black Pepper: A pinch (tolerated by few patients; Substitution: Omit if intolerant)

Instructions:

- Steam the cauliflower florets until very tender, about 15 minutes.

- In a blender, combine the steamed cauliflower, turmeric powder, olive oil, and a small amount of the vegetable broth or water.
- Blend until the mixture becomes completely smooth, adding more broth or water as needed to achieve the desired consistency.
- Season with a pinch of black pepper or omit according to tolerance.
- Serve warm, ensuring the puree's consistency is suitable for a Level 1 dysphagia diet.

Scientific Notes:

- Cauliflower: Offers a high nutritional profile, including vitamins C and K, and fiber, which supports digestive health.
- Turmeric Powder: Contains curcumin, known for its anti-inflammatory and antioxidant properties, potentially beneficial for overall health.
- Olive Oil: A healthy fat source that helps to improve puree texture and supports heart health.
- Black Pepper: When tolerated, can enhance nutrient absorption, particularly the bioavailability of curcumin from turmeric.

Nutritional Information (per serving):

- Calories: Approximately 180
- Protein: 3g
- Total Fat: 14g
- Saturated Fat: 2g
- Carbohydrates: 13g
- Fiber: 5g
- Sodium: 30mg (may vary with broth selection)

7 DAYS MEAL PLAN FOR PHASE 1

Day 1:

Breakfast: Pureed Butternut Squash Soup

Lunch: Creamy Potato and Leek Soup Puree

Dinner: Silky Mango and Coconut Puree

Day 2:

Breakfast: Smooth Carrot and Ginger Puree

Lunch: Smooth Pumpkin Puree

Dinner: Velvety Sweet Potato and Carrot Puree

Day 3:

Breakfast: Creamy Avocado and Spinach Puree

Lunch: Silken Tofu and Berry Puree

Dinner: Creamed Spinach and White Bean Puree

Day 4:

Breakfast: Silky Pear Puree

Lunch: Pear and Avocado Puree

Dinner: Butternut Squash and Apple Puree

Day 5:

Breakfast: Blueberry Banana Smoothie Puree

Lunch: Creamy Broccoli and Potato Puree

Dinner: Cauliflower and Turmeric Puree

Day 6: (Reintroduce favorites with slight variations if possible)

Breakfast: Smooth Carrot and Ginger Puree with a hint of cinnamon

Lunch: Creamy Potato and Leek Soup Puree with added parsley

Dinner: Silky Mango and Coconut Puree with a splash of lime

Day 7: (Mix and match to explore new flavor combinations)

Breakfast: A mix of Silky Pear Puree and Blueberry Banana Smoothie Puree

Lunch: Combination of Silken Tofu and Berry Puree with Creamy Broccoli and Potato Puree

Dinner: Mix of Creamed Spinach and White Bean Puree with Cauliflower and Turmeric Puree

7 DAYS MEAL PLANNER

NEGLECT THE SNACKS AND APPETIZER

AMOS JIMMY
DAILY MEAL PLANNER

DATE ————————————————   M T W T F S S
:

BREAKFAST

DINNER

LUNCH

NOTES

SNACKS

JIMMY'S CULINARY HAVEN

CELEBRATING YOUR JOURNEY INTO PHASE 2 [SOFT FOOD RECIPES FOR DYSPHAGIA]

As we transition from the Phase 1 Pureed Diet in our Dysphagia Diet Guide, we are thrilled to introduce a selection of soft food recipes for breakfast, perfect for those progressing to Phase 2 of the dysphagia diet. This guide is designed to support individuals facing swallowing difficulties, offering nutritious and enjoyable meal options that cater to various dietary preferences, including choices for those who prefer more or less meat.

Each recipe has been meticulously designed to align with the nutritional needs and safety requirements of individuals with dysphagia, ensuring you can savor delicious meals while prioritizing your swallowing health. Incorporating these meals into your daily routine represents a significant step forward in managing your condition effectively and enhancing your overall well-being.

As we look forward to presenting you with an assortment of soft food breakfast, lunch and dinner recipes in the next chapter, we invite you to share your valuable feedback with us. Your insights and experiences are crucial in helping us refine our meal plans and ensure they meet your dietary requirements, enabling more individuals to navigate their dysphagia diet with confidence and success

We extend our heartfelt thanks for your dedication to improving your health through the Dysphagia Diet approach. Your active participation and commitment to this dietary strategy are vital to our community's success. As we move forward to the next phase, which promises even more flavorful and health-conscious meal options, we eagerly anticipate your continued engagement and feedback.

CHAPTER 3

BREAKFAST RECIPES LEVEL 2 (SOFT FOOD)

Soft Baked Salmon with Mashed Sweet Potato

Serves: 1

Cooking Time: 30 minutes

Ingredients and Portions/Measurements:

- Salmon Fillet (soft food friendly): 4 oz (Substitution: Canned salmon for easier preparation)
- Sweet Potato (soft food friendly): 1 medium, peeled
- Olive Oil: 1 teaspoon
- Lemon Juice: 1 tablespoon (Substitution: A pinch of citric acid for those sensitive to citrus)
- Dill: 1 teaspoon, chopped (soft food friendly)
- Salt: A pinch (Substitution: Potassium chloride for those on a sodium-restricted diet)
- Black Pepper: A pinch (omit if not tolerated)

Instructions:

- Preheat your oven to 375°F (190°C). Place the salmon on a baking sheet lined with parchment paper. Drizzle with olive oil and lemon juice (or citric acid). Season with a pinch of salt (or potassium chloride) and black pepper if tolerated. Sprinkle chopped dill over the top.
- Bake the salmon for 20-25 minutes, or until it flakes easily with a fork.
- While the salmon is baking, boil the sweet potato in water until tender. Drain and mash the sweet potato with a fork or potato masher until smooth. Season with a little olive oil, salt (or potassium chloride), and black pepper to taste.
- Serve the baked salmon alongside the mashed sweet potato. Ensure the salmon is flaked into small, manageable pieces for easier chewing and swallowing.

Scientific Notes:

- Salmon: Rich in omega-3 fatty acids, which are beneficial for heart health, and a good source of protein for muscle maintenance.
- Sweet Potato: High in beta-carotene (vitamin A precursor), vitamins C and B6, and fiber, supporting vision, immune function, and digestive health.

- Olive Oil: Provides monounsaturated fats, beneficial for heart health, and helps achieve a smoother consistency in mashed sweet potatoes.

Nutritional Information (per serving):

- Calories: Approximately 350
- Protein: 25g
- Total Fat: 15g
- Saturated Fat: 2.5g
- Carbohydrates: 35g
- Fiber: 5g
- Sodium: 70mg (may vary with substitutions)

Soft-Cooked Chicken and Vegetable Stew

Serves: 1

Cooking Time: 40 minutes

Ingredients and Portions/Measurements:

- Chicken Breast (soft food friendly): 4 oz, diced
- Carrots (soft food friendly): 1/2 cup, peeled and sliced
- Zucchini (soft food friendly): 1/2 cup, diced
- Low-Sodium Chicken Broth: 1 cup (Substitution: Water with a pinch of salt substitute for those on a sodium-restricted diet)
- Thyme: 1 teaspoon (soft food friendly)
- Olive Oil: 1 teaspoon
- Salt: A pinch (Substitution: Potassium chloride)
- Black Pepper: A pinch (omit if not tolerated)

Instructions:

- In a pot, heat the olive oil over medium heat. Add the diced chicken breast and cook until it's no longer pink on the outside.
- Add the sliced carrots, diced zucchini, thyme, and low-sodium chicken broth (or water with a pinch of salt substitute). Bring to a boil, then reduce heat and

simmer until the vegetables are very soft and the chicken is thoroughly cooked, about 30 minutes.

- Before serving, check the stew's consistency. The vegetables and chicken should be tender enough to mash with a fork, ensuring they're soft and easy to chew.
- Season with a pinch of salt (or potassium chloride) and black pepper to taste, if tolerated.

Scientific Notes:

- Chicken Breast: A lean source of protein, essential for muscle repair and maintenance.
- Carrots and Zucchini: Provide a mix of vitamins, minerals, and fiber, promoting eye health, immune function, and digestive health.
- Olive Oil: Adds healthy fats and helps keep the stew moist, making it easier to swallow.

Nutritional Information (per serving):

- Calories: Approximately 300
- Protein: 28g
- Total Fat: 10g
- Saturated Fat: 1.5g
- Carbohydrates: 20g

- Fiber: 4g
- Sodium: 100mg (may vary with substitutions)

Soft Poached Egg with Avocado Toast

Serves: 1

Cooking Time: 10 minutes

Ingredients and Portions/Measurements:

- Egg (soft food friendly): 1 large (Substitution: Egg substitute for those with egg allergies)
- Avocado (soft food friendly): 1/2 ripe avocado
- Soft Whole Grain Bread: 1 slice (Substitution: Gluten-free bread for those with gluten intolerance)
- Olive Oil: A drizzle
- Ground Paprika: A pinch (omit if not tolerated)
- Salt: A pinch (Substitution: Potassium chloride for those on a sodium-restricted diet)

Instructions:

- Bring a pot of water to a light simmer. Carefully crack the egg into the water. Poach for about 3-4 minutes until the whites are set but the yolk remains runny. Remove with a slotted spoon and set aside on a paper towel.

- Mash the avocado with a fork and spread it onto the soft whole grain or gluten-free bread.
- Gently place the poached egg on top of the mashed avocado.
- Drizzle with olive oil and sprinkle a pinch of ground paprika and salt (or potassium chloride) over it, if tolerated.
- Ensure the bread is soft and the egg is cooked to a soft consistency to comply with a Level 2 dysphagia diet.

Scientific Notes:

- Egg: High-quality protein source that supports muscle repair and growth. Eggs are also a good source of vitamins D and B12.
- Avocado: Provides healthy fats, fiber, and vitamins E, K, and C, promoting heart health and aiding digestion.
- Whole Grain Bread: Offers dietary fiber and B vitamins. Gluten-free options ensure accessibility for those with gluten intolerance.

Nutritional Information (per serving):

- Calories: Approximately 300
- Protein: 10g

- Total Fat: 20g
- Saturated Fat: 3.5g
- Carbohydrates: 20g
- Fiber: 5g
- Sodium: 100mg (varies with substitutions)

Tender Turkey Meatballs with Soft-Cooked Carrots

Serves: 1

Cooking Time: 30 minutes

Ingredients and Portions/Measurements:

- Ground Turkey (soft food friendly): 4 oz (Substitution: Ground chicken for those with turkey sensitivities)
- Bread Crumbs: 2 tablespoons (Substitution: Gluten-free bread crumbs)
- Egg: 1 (Substitution: 1 tablespoon of flaxseed meal mixed with 2.5 tablespoons of water for an egg-free option)
- Carrots: 2 medium, peeled and sliced
- Olive Oil: 1 teaspoon
- Thyme: 1/2 teaspoon (soft food friendly)

- Salt: A pinch (Substitution: Potassium chloride)
- Black Pepper: A pinch (omit if not tolerated)

Instructions:

- Preheat your oven to 375°F (190°C). In a bowl, mix ground turkey with bread crumbs, the egg (or flaxseed meal mixture), thyme, and a pinch of salt (or potassium chloride) and black pepper if tolerated. Form into small meatballs.
- Place meatballs on a baking tray lined with parchment paper and brush with olive oil.
- Bake for 20-25 minutes or until cooked through and tender.
- Steam the sliced carrots until very soft, about 10-15 minutes.
- Serve the tender meatballs alongside the soft-cooked carrots, ensuring both are easy to chew and swallow.

Scientific Notes:

- Ground Turkey/Chicken: Lean protein sources are essential for muscle maintenance and repair. Poultry is also a source of various vitamins and minerals.

- Carrots: High in beta-carotene, which the body converts into vitamin A, supporting eye health and immune function.
- Olive Oil: Contains monounsaturated fats beneficial for heart health and helps maintain moisture in the meatballs, making them easier to chew.

Nutritional Information (per serving):

- Calories: Approximately 350
- Protein: 24g
- Total Fat: 18g
- Saturated Fat: 3g
- Carbohydrates: 20g
- Fiber: 3g
- Sodium: 200mg (may vary with substitutions)

Soft Lentil Patties with Yogurt Sauce

Serves: 1

Cooking Time: 30 minutes

Ingredients and Portions/Measurements:

- Cooked Lentils (soft food friendly): 1/2 cup (Substitution: Mashed chickpeas for a different texture and taste)
- Bread Crumbs: 1 tablespoon (Substitution: Gluten-free bread crumbs)
- Egg: 1, beaten (Substitution: 1 tablespoon ground flaxseed mixed with 3 tablespoons water for an egg-free option)
- Cumin: 1/4 teaspoon (soft food friendly)
- Olive Oil: For cooking
- Plain Yogurt: 2 tablespoons (Substitution: Coconut yogurt for a dairy-free option)
- Garlic Powder: A pinch (Substitution: A pinch of asafoetida for those with garlic sensitivities)
- Salt: A pinch (Substitution: Potassium chloride for those on a sodium-restricted diet)

Instructions:

- In a mixing bowl, combine the cooked lentils, bread crumbs (or gluten-free alternative), beaten egg (or flaxseed mixture), cumin, and a pinch of salt (or potassium chloride). Mix until well combined.
- Form the mixture into small patties.
- Heat olive oil in a non-stick pan over medium heat. Cook the patties for about 3-4 minutes on each side until they are golden brown and firm.
- Mix the plain yogurt (or coconut yogurt) with garlic powder (or asafoetida) in a small bowl for the sauce.
- Serve the soft lentil patties with the yogurt sauce on the side.

Scientific Notes:

- Lentils: A great source of protein, fiber, and minerals such as iron and magnesium, supporting muscle health and digestion.
- Yogurt: Provides calcium and probiotics, which are beneficial for bone health and digestive wellness.
- Cumin: Known for its digestive benefits and adds flavor without the need for additional salt.

Nutritional Information (per serving):

- Calories: Approximately 250
- Protein: 14g
- Total Fat: 9g (varies with the amount of olive oil used)
- Saturated Fat: 1.5g
- Carbohydrates: 30g
- Fiber: 6g
- Sodium: 200mg (may vary with substitutions)

LUNCH RECIPES LEVEL 2 (SOFT FOOD)

Creamy Butternut Squash Soup

Serves: 1

Cooking Time: 45 minutes

Ingredients and Portions/Measurements:

- Butternut Squash (soft food friendly): 1 cup, peeled and cubed
- Vegetable Broth: 1 cup (Substitution: Low-sodium broth for those on a sodium-restricted diet)
- Onion: 1/4 cup, finely chopped (soft food friendly)
- Olive Oil: 1 teaspoon
- Nutmeg: A pinch
- Salt: A pinch (Substitution: Potassium chloride)
- Pepper: A pinch (omit if not tolerated)

Instructions:

- In a pot, heat the olive oil over medium heat. Add the chopped onion and cook until translucent.
- Add the cubed butternut squash and cook for a few minutes, stirring occasionally.

- Add the vegetable broth and bring to a boil. Reduce heat and simmer until the squash is very soft, about 30 minutes.
- Puree the mixture using a blender or an immersion blender until smooth.
- Return the soup to the pot and reheat gently. Season with nutmeg, salt (or potassium chloride), and pepper to taste, if tolerated.
- Serve warm, ensuring the soup is smooth and velvety, suitable for a Level 2 dysphagia diet.

Scientific Notes:

- Butternut Squash: High in vitamins A and C, promoting eye health and immune function. The smooth texture of the soup is ideal for those on a soft food diet.
- Olive Oil: Contains healthy monounsaturated fats, supporting heart health.
- Nutmeg: Adds flavor and has been associated with digestive health benefits.

Nutritional Information (per serving):

- Calories: Approximately 150
- Protein: 2g

- Total Fat: 5g
- Saturated Fat: 0.7g
- Carbohydrates: 25g
- Fiber: 4g
- Sodium: 500mg (may vary with broth selection)

Gentle Beef and Broccoli Stir-Fry

Serves: 1

Cooking Time: 20 minutes

Ingredients and Portions/Measurements:

- Lean Ground Beef (soft food friendly): 4 oz (Substitution: Ground turkey for those with beef sensitivities)
- Broccoli Florets: 1/2 cup, steamed until very soft (Substitution: Cauliflower for those with broccoli sensitivities)
- Olive Oil: 1 teaspoon
- Soy Sauce: 1 tablespoon (Substitution: Low-sodium soy sauce or a soy-free alternative like coconut aminos)
- Garlic Powder: 1/4 teaspoon (Substitution: A pinch of asafoetida for those with garlic sensitivities)
- Ginger Powder: 1/4 teaspoon (soft food friendly)

- Cooked Rice: 1/2 cup (Substitution: Cooked quinoa for a gluten-free option)

Instructions:

- Heat olive oil in a skillet over medium heat. Add the ground beef (or turkey) and cook until browned, breaking it into small, soft pieces as it cooks.
- Add the steamed broccoli (or cauliflower) to the skillet with the beef. Stir in soy sauce (or coconut aminos), garlic powder (or asafoetida), and ginger powder. Cook for an additional 5 minutes, ensuring the broccoli is tender and the flavors meld.
- Serve the beef and broccoli stir-fry over cooked rice (or quinoa), ensuring all components are soft and easy to chew.

Scientific Notes:

- Lean Ground Beef/Turkey: Provides high-quality protein essential for muscle maintenance and repair. Lean meats are easier to digest and chew when cooked properly.
- Broccoli/Cauliflower: Both are high in vitamins C and K and provide dietary fiber that supports digestion.

Ensure they are cooked until very soft for easier swallowing.

- Ginger: Known for its anti-inflammatory properties and can aid digestion.

Nutritional Information (per serving):

- Calories: Approximately 400
- Protein: 26g
- Total Fat: 12g
- Saturated Fat: 3g
- Carbohydrates: 45g
- Fiber: 3g
- Sodium: 700mg (may vary with soy sauce alternative)

Soft-Cooked Pasta with Creamy Pumpkin Sauce

Serves: 1

Cooking Time: 25 minutes

Ingredients and Portions/Measurements:

- Pasta (soft food friendly): 1 cup (Substitution: Gluten-free pasta for those with gluten intolerance)
- Pumpkin Puree: 1/2 cup
- Heavy Cream: 1/4 cup (Substitution: Coconut cream for a dairy-free option)
- Nutmeg: A pinch (soft food friendly)
- Parmesan Cheese: 1 tablespoon, grated (Substitution: Nutritional yeast for a dairy-free option)
- Salt: A pinch (Substitution: Potassium chloride for those on a sodium-restricted diet)
- Black Pepper: A pinch (omit if not tolerated)

Instructions:

- Cook pasta according to package instructions until it is very soft. Drain and set aside.
- In a saucepan, combine pumpkin puree, heavy cream (or coconut cream), nutmeg, and a pinch of salt (or

potassium chloride). Heat over medium until the sauce is warm and smooth.

- Toss the soft-cooked pasta in the pumpkin sauce until evenly coated.
- Serve the pasta topped with grated Parmesan cheese (or nutritional yeast) and a pinch of black pepper, if tolerated.

Scientific Notes:

- Pumpkin Puree: A good source of vitamins A and C, fiber, and potassium, supporting eye health, immune function, and digestion.
- Heavy Cream/Coconut Cream: Adds richness and calories for energy. Coconut cream offers a lactose-free fat source.
- Parmesan Cheese/Nutritional Yeast: Parmesan adds flavor and calcium, while nutritional yeast provides B vitamins and a cheese-like flavor for those avoiding dairy.

Nutritional Information (per serving):

- Calories: Approximately 450
- Protein: 12g
- Total Fat: 20g

- Saturated Fat: 12g (varies with cream substitution)
- Carbohydrates: 55g
- Fiber: 4g
- Sodium: 300mg (may vary with substitutions)

Soft Pear and Cottage Cheese Salad

Serves: 1

Cooking Time: 10 minutes

Ingredients and Portions/Measurements:

- Pear (soft food friendly): 1 ripe pear, peeled and diced
- Cottage Cheese: 1/2 cup (Substitution: Ricotta cheese for a smoother texture)
- Honey: 1 teaspoon (Substitution: Maple syrup for vegans)
- Cinnamon: A pinch (soft food friendly)
- Walnuts: 1 tablespoon, finely chopped (omit if nut allergies are a concern or substitute with soft seeds like pumpkin seeds for texture)

Instructions:

- In a bowl, mix the diced pear with cottage cheese (or ricotta).

- Drizzle honey (or maple syrup) over the pear and cheese mixture.
- Sprinkle with a pinch of cinnamon and add the finely chopped walnuts (or substitute).
- Gently mix to combine all ingredients.
- Serve immediately, ensuring the pear is soft enough for easy chewing and the nuts/seeds are finely chopped to prevent any swallowing difficulties.

Scientific Notes:

- Pear: High in fiber and vitamin C, pears can aid digestion and support the immune system. Ensure the pear is ripe for softness.
- Cottage Cheese/Ricotta Cheese: Good sources of calcium and protein, supporting bone health and muscle repair. Ricotta can offer a smoother consistency if needed.
- Honey/Maple Syrup: Both are natural sweeteners; maple syrup offers an alternative for those avoiding animal products.
- Walnuts/Pumpkin Seeds: Provide healthy fats and a texture contrast. Ensure they are finely chopped or omitted based on individual tolerance.

Nutritional Information (per serving):

- Calories: Approximately 200
- Protein: 12g
- Total Fat: 8g
- Saturated Fat: 3g
- Carbohydrates: 22g
- Fiber: 3g
- Sodium: 400mg (varies with cheese selection)

Tender Chicken and Rice Porridge

Serves: 1

Cooking Time: 45 minutes

Ingredients and Portions/Measurements:

- Chicken Breast (soft food friendly): 4 oz, finely chopped
- White Rice: 1/4 cup (Substitution: Brown rice for more fiber, note longer cooking time)
- Chicken Broth: 2 cups (Substitution: Low-sodium broth or vegetable broth)
- Ginger: 1 teaspoon, grated (soft food friendly)
- Salt: A pinch (Substitution: Potassium chloride for those on a sodium-restricted diet)

Instructions:

- Combine the chicken broth, rice, and grated ginger in a pot. Bring to a boil.
- Reduce the heat to low and add the finely chopped chicken breast to the pot.
- Simmer on low heat, stirring occasionally, until the rice is very soft and the mixture has a porridge-like consistency, about 30-40 minutes.

- Season with a pinch of salt (or potassium chloride) to taste.
- Serve warm, ensuring the porridge is thoroughly cooked for easy swallowing.

Scientific Notes:

- Chicken Breast: Provides lean protein necessary for muscle repair and maintenance.
- White/Brown Rice: A good source of carbohydrates for energy. Brown rice offers additional fiber but requires a longer cooking time to achieve a soft texture.
- Ginger: Known for its anti-inflammatory properties and can aid in digestion.

Nutritional Information (per serving):

- Calories: Approximately 300
- Protein: 26g
- Total Fat: 3g
- Saturated Fat: 0.5g
- Carbohydrates: 40g
- Fiber: 1g (higher with brown rice)
- Sodium: 600mg (may vary with broth selection)

DINNER RECIPES LEVEL 2 (SOFT FOOD)

Soft Vegetable Omelet

Serves: 1

Cooking Time: minutes

Ingredients and Portions/Measurements:

- Eggs: 2 large (Substitution: Liquid egg substitute for those with egg allergies)
- Milk: 2 tablespoons (Substitution: Almond milk for dairy-free option)
- Spinach: 1/4 cup, chopped and steamed until very soft
- Bell Pepper: 1/4 cup, finely diced and sautéed until soft
- Cheddar Cheese: 1 tablespoon, grated (Substitution: Dairy-free cheese)
- Olive Oil: For cooking
- Salt: A pinch (Substitution: Potassium chloride for those on a sodium-restricted diet)
- Black Pepper: A pinch (omit if not tolerated)

Instructions:

- In a bowl, whisk the eggs (or egg substitute) with milk (or almond milk). Season with a pinch of salt (or potassium chloride) and black pepper, if tolerated.
- Heat a non-stick skillet over medium heat and add a bit of olive oil.
- Pour the egg mixture into the skillet, allowing it to set slightly before scattering the soft spinach, bell pepper, and cheddar cheese (or substitute) over the top.
- Gently fold the omelet in half and continue cooking until the eggs are set and the cheese has melted.
- Serve warm, ensuring the omelet is thoroughly cooked and soft, suitable for a Level 2 dysphagia diet.

Scientific Notes:

- Eggs: Provide high-quality protein and essential nutrients, including vitamins D and B12.
- Spinach and Bell Pepper: Offer vitamins A, C, and K, along with fiber, which are important for immune health and digestion.
- Milk/Almond Milk: Adds calcium (dairy milk) or vitamin D (fortified almond milk), both essential for bone health.

Nutritional Information (per serving):

- Calories: Approximately 250
- Protein: 16g
- Total Fat: 18g
- Saturated Fat: 5g
- Carbohydrates: 6g
- Fiber: 1g
- Sodium: 320mg (varies with substitutions)

Soft Poached Pear in Cinnamon Syrup

Serves: 1

Cooking Time: 25 minutes

Ingredients and Portions/Measurements:

- Pear: 1 large, peeled (Substitution: Apple for a different flavor)
- Water: 1 cup
- Cinnamon Stick: 1 (soft food friendly)
- Cloves: 2 (Substitution: Ground cloves, but strain before serving)
- Honey: 1 tablespoon (Substitution: Maple syrup for vegans)

Instructions:

- In a small saucepan, combine water, the cinnamon stick, cloves (or a pinch of ground cloves), and honey (or maple syrup). Bring to a simmer.
- Add the peeled pear to the saucepan and cover. Poach the pear over low heat for about 20 minutes or until it is very soft.
- Carefully remove the pear from the syrup and let it cool slightly.

- Serve the soft poached pear with a drizzle of the cinnamon syrup.
- Ensure the pear is soft enough for easy chewing and swallowing, suitable for a Level 2 dysphagia diet.

Scientific Notes:

- Pear: A good source of dietary fiber and vitamin C, aiding in digestion and supporting the immune system.
- Cinnamon: Known for its anti-inflammatory properties and can help regulate blood sugar levels.
- Honey/Maple Syrup: Natural sweeteners; maple syrup is a good alternative for those avoiding honey due to dietary preferences.

Nutritional Information (per serving):

- Calories: Approximately 150
- Protein: 0.5g
- Total Fat: 0g
- Saturated Fat: 0g
- Carbohydrates: 38g
- Fiber: 5g
- Sodium: 10mg

Soft Baked Fish with Herbed Potato Mash

Serves: 1

Cooking Time: 30 minutes

Ingredients and Portions/Measurements:

- White Fish Fillet (soft food friendly): 4 oz (Substitution: Canned tuna for those who prefer or need an easier option)
- Potatoes: 1 large, peeled and cubed
- Milk: 2 tablespoons (Substitution: Almond milk for a dairy-free option)
- Butter: 1 teaspoon (Substitution: Olive oil for a dairy-free option)
- Dill: 1/2 teaspoon, finely chopped (soft food friendly)
- Lemon Juice: 1 teaspoon (Substitution: A pinch of citric acid for those sensitive to citrus)
- Salt: A pinch (Substitution: Potassium chloride for those on a sodium-restricted diet)
- Black Pepper: A pinch (omit if not tolerated)

Instructions:

- Preheat the oven to 350°F (175°C). Place the fish fillet on a baking sheet lined with parchment paper. Drizzle with lemon juice (or citric acid) and sprinkle with dill. Bake for 20 minutes or until the fish flakes easily with a fork.

- While the fish is baking, boil the cubed potatoes until very soft, about 15-20 minutes. Drain and return to the pot.
- Add milk (or almond milk) and butter (or olive oil) to the potatoes. Mash until smooth and creamy. Season with salt (or potassium chloride) and black pepper to taste.
- Serve the soft baked fish over the herbed potato mash, ensuring both components are soft enough to meet the needs of a Level 2 dysphagia diet.

Scientific Notes:

- White Fish: Provides high-quality protein and is typically low in fat, making it easy to digest and beneficial for muscle maintenance.
- Potatoes: A good source of carbohydrates, potassium, and vitamin C, supporting energy levels and immune health.

Nutritional Information (per serving):

- Calories: Approximately 300

- Protein: 26g
- Total Fat: 6g
- Saturated Fat: 2g
- Carbohydrates: 34g
- Fiber: 3g
- Sodium: 200mg (may vary with substitutions)

Soft Spinach and Ricotta Stuffed Pasta Shells

Serves: 1

Cooking Time: 45 minutes

Ingredients and Portions/Measurements:

- Large Pasta Shells: 4 pieces (Substitution: Gluten-free pasta shells for those with gluten intolerance)
- Ricotta Cheese: 1/2 cup (Substitution: Silken tofu for a dairy-free option)
- Spinach: 1/2 cup, steamed and finely chopped (pureed dysphagia diet friendly)
- Egg: 1 small, beaten (Substitution: 1 tablespoon of chia seeds mixed with 3 tablespoons water, let sit until gelatinous for an egg-free option)
- Parmesan Cheese: 1 tablespoon, grated (Substitution: Nutritional yeast for a dairy-free option)
- Marinara Sauce: 1/2 cup (Substitution: Blended roasted red peppers for a nightshade-free option)
- Salt: A pinch (Substitution: Potassium chloride for those on a sodium-restricted diet)
- Black Pepper: A pinch (omit if not tolerated)

Instructions:

- Preheat the oven to 350°F (175°C). Cook the pasta shells according to package instructions until they are just tender. Drain and set aside to cool.
- In a bowl, mix the ricotta cheese (or silken tofu) with the steamed, finely chopped spinach, beaten egg (or chia mixture), a pinch of salt (or potassium chloride), and black pepper if tolerated.
- Carefully stuff each pasta shell with the spinach and ricotta mixture.
- Spread a thin layer of marinara sauce (or blended roasted red pepper sauce) on the bottom of a baking dish.
- Place the stuffed pasta shells in the dish. Cover with the remaining sauce.
- Sprinkle grated Parmesan cheese (or nutritional yeast) over the top.
- Bake covered for 30 minutes, then uncover and bake for an additional 5-10 minutes until the top is slightly golden and the filling is heated through.
- Ensure the final dish is soft and moist, suitable for a Level 2 dysphagia diet.

Scientific Notes:

- Spinach: Provides vitamins A, C, K, iron, and folate, supporting immune function, bone health, and red blood cell production.
- Ricotta Cheese/Silken Tofu: Ricotta is rich in protein and calcium, important for bone health. Silken tofu offers a plant-based protein alternative, also providing a soft texture ideal for those on a soft food diet.
- Egg/Chia Seeds: Eggs are a complete protein source. Chia seeds are rich in omega-3 fatty acids, fiber, and can be used as a binding agent in egg-free diets.

Nutritional Information (per serving):

- Calories: Approximately 350
- Protein: 18g
- Total Fat: 16g
- Saturated Fat: 8g (varies with substitutions)
- Carbohydrates: 35g
- Fiber: 4g
- Sodium: 500mg (may vary with substitutions)

Soft Baked Chicken Breast

Serves: 1

Cooking Time: 25 minutes

Ingredients and Portions/Measurements:

- Chicken Breast (skinless and boneless): 150g (High in protein, suitable for dysphagia patients needing soft, easily chewable food)
- Olive Oil: 1 tablespoon (For cooking, provides healthy fats)
- Garlic Powder: ½ teaspoon (For flavor, easier on the digestive system than raw garlic)
- Cooked Carrot Puree: ¼ cup (As a side, high in vitamin A and fiber, dysphagia-friendly)
- Thyme: To taste (For flavor, antioxidant properties)

Instructions:

- Preheat your oven to 350°F (175°C).
- Rub the chicken breast with olive oil, garlic powder, and thyme.
- Place the chicken in a baking dish and bake for 20-25 minutes, or until the internal temperature reaches 165°F (74°C).

- Serve with carrot puree on the side.

Scientific Notes:

- Chicken Breast: A lean source of protein that's essential for muscle repair and maintenance. For dysphagia diets, it's important that the chicken is cooked until tender and easily shredded for easier swallowing.
- Olive Oil: Contains monounsaturated fats, known to support heart health. It also makes the chicken moist, aiding in easier swallowing.
- Garlic Powder: Offers flavor without the risk of choking on garlic pieces. Garlic has antimicrobial properties and may support immune health.
- Carrot Puree: Soft, easy to swallow, and rich in vitamin A for eye health and immune function. The puree form is ideal for dysphagia patients to ensure safe swallowing.
- Thyme: An herb with antimicrobial and antioxidant properties. Adds flavor without needing to add salt, which is beneficial for managing blood pressure.

Nutritional Information (per serving):

- Calories: Approx. 300
- Protein: 26g
- Total Fat: 14g (mostly from olive oil, a healthy fat)
- Saturated Fat: Low
- Carbohydrates: 8g (from carrot puree)
- Sodium: Low

7 DAYS MEAL PLAN FOR PHASE 2

Day 1

Breakfast: Soft Baked Salmon with Mashed Sweet Potato

Lunch: Creamy Butternut Squash Soup

Dinner: Soft Vegetable Omelet

Day 2

Breakfast: Soft Poached Egg with Avocado Toast

Lunch: Gentle Beef and Broccoli Stir-Fry

Dinner: Soft Baked Fish with Herbed Potato Mash

Day 3

Breakfast: Tender Turkey Meatballs with Soft-Cooked Carrots

Lunch: Soft-Cooked Pasta with Creamy Pumpkin Sauce

Dinner: Creamy Carrot and Ginger Soup

Day 4

Breakfast: Soft Lentil Patties with Yogurt Sauce

Lunch: Soft Pear and Cottage Cheese Salad

Dinner: Soft Spinach and Ricotta Stuffed Pasta Shells

Day 5

Breakfast: Soft-Cooked Chicken and Vegetable Stew

Lunch: Tender Chicken and Rice Porridge

Dinner: Soft Baked Chicken Breast

Day 6

Breakfast: Soft Poached Egg with Avocado Toast

Lunch: Creamy Butternut Squash Soup

Dinner: Soft Baked Fish with Herbed Potato Mash

Day 7

Breakfast: Soft Baked Salmon with Mashed Sweet Potato

Lunch: Soft-Cooked Pasta with Creamy Pumpkin Sauce

Dinner: Soft Poached Pear in Cinnamon Syrup

7 DAYS MEAL PLANNER

NEGLECT THE SNACKS AND APPETIZER

AMOS JIMMY

DAILY MEAL PLANNER

DATE _____ :   M T W T F S S

BREAKFAST

DINNER

LUNCH

NOTES

SNACKS

JIMMY'S CULINARY HAVEN

CHAPTER 4

BREAKFAST RECIPES LEVEL 3 [ADVANCED DIET]

Creamy Carrot and Ginger Soup

Serves: 1

Cooking Time: 35 minutes

Ingredients and Portions/Measurements:

- Carrots: 2 large, peeled and chopped
- Ginger: 1 teaspoon, grated (soft food friendly)
- Vegetable Broth: 1 cup (Substitution: Low-sodium vegetable broth for those monitoring sodium intake)
- Coconut Milk: 1/4 cup (for creaminess and a dairy-free option)
- Salt: A pinch (Substitution: Potassium chloride)
- Black Pepper: A pinch (omit if not tolerated)

Instructions:

- In a pot, combine the chopped carrots, grated ginger, and vegetable broth. Bring to a boil, then reduce heat and simmer until the carrots are very soft, about 25 minutes.
- Use an immersion blender or transfer to a blender to puree the soup until smooth.
- Stir in the coconut milk and warm the soup through. Season with salt (or potassium chloride) and black pepper to taste.
- Serve warm, ensuring the soup's consistency is smooth and suitable for those on a Level 2 dysphagia diet.

Scientific Notes:

Carrots: High in beta-carotene, which is converted to vitamin A in the body, supporting eye health and immune function.

Ginger: Known for its anti-inflammatory properties and gastrointestinal benefits, aiding in digestion.

Nutritional Information (per serving):

- Calories: Approximately 180
- Protein: 2g

- Total Fat: 9g
- Saturated Fat: 7g (from coconut milk)
- Carbohydrates: 24g
- Fiber: 5g
- Sodium: 300mg (may vary with broth selection)

Creamy Avocado and Spinach Pasta

Serves: 1

Cooking Time: 20 minutes

Ingredients and Portions/Measurements:

- Cooked Pasta (preferably a soft type like penne or fusilli): 1 cup (Provides carbohydrates for energy, easy to chew and swallow for dysphagia patients)
- Ripe Avocado: ½ (Provides healthy fats, creamy texture makes it easier to swallow)
- Spinach: ½ cup, steamed and pureed (Rich in iron and vitamins, blended for easy swallowing)
- Lemon Juice: 1 teaspoon (Adds flavor, vitamin C for immune support)
- Garlic Powder: ¼ teaspoon (For flavor, easier to digest than raw garlic)

Instructions:

- Cook pasta according to package instructions until very soft. Drain.
- In a blender, combine the avocado, pureed spinach, lemon juice, and garlic powder. Blend until smooth.
- Toss the cooked pasta with the avocado-spinach sauce until well coated.
- Serve warm.

Scientific Notes:

- Pasta: Carbohydrates are essential for energy. Choosing softer pasta ensures it is safer and easier for dysphagia patients to eat.
- Avocado: High in monounsaturated fats, contributing to heart health. Its creamy texture helps in creating sauces that are easier to swallow.
- Spinach: Pureeing spinach makes it easier to swallow and ensures that patients can still benefit from its high nutrient content, including iron, magnesium, and vitamins A and C.
- Lemon Juice: Adds flavor without salt and provides vitamin C, which is important for immune health and iron absorption.

- Garlic Powder: Used instead of raw garlic to avoid choking hazards while still adding flavor and benefiting from its antimicrobial properties.

Nutritional Information (per serving):

- Calories: Approx. 400
- Protein: 10g
- Total Fat: 22g (mostly from avocado, a healthy fat)
- Saturated Fat: Low
- Carbohydrates: 44g
- Sodium: Low

Quinoa Porridge with Almond Milk

Serves: 1

Cooking Time: 15 minutes

Ingredients and Portions/Measurements:

- Quinoa: ½ cup (High in protein and fiber, gluten-free, easy to digest)
- Almond Milk: 1 cup (Dairy-free, adds creaminess without lactose)
- Maple Syrup: 1 tablespoon (Natural sweetener, easier on the digestive system than refined sugars)
- Ground Cinnamon: ¼ teaspoon (For flavor, anti-inflammatory properties)
- Banana Puree: ¼ cup (Soft, easy to swallow, high in potassium)

Instructions:

- Rinse quinoa under cold water.
- In a pot, bring almond milk to a boil, add quinoa and reduce to a simmer. Cover and cook for 15 minutes, or until quinoa is soft and has absorbed most of the liquid.

- Stir in maple syrup, ground cinnamon, and banana puree.
- Serve warm.

Scientific Notes:

- Quinoa: A complete protein containing all nine essential amino acids, important for tissue repair and growth. Its soft texture upon cooking makes it suitable for dysphagia diets.
- Almond Milk: A lactose-free alternative to cow's milk, making it suitable for those with lactose intolerance. It contributes to the creamy texture of the porridge.
- Maple Syrup: Provides sweetness with a lower glycemic index than sugar, making it a better option for maintaining stable blood sugar levels.
- Ground Cinnamon: Adds flavor and has anti-inflammatory properties, which may benefit overall health.
- Banana Puree: Bananas are high in potassium, which is essential for heart health and muscle function. Pureeing the banana ensures it is easy to swallow.

Nutritional Information (per serving):

- Calories: Approx. 350
- Protein: 8g
- Total Fat: 5g (from almond milk)
- Saturated Fat: Low
- Carbohydrates: 65g
- Sodium: Low

Tender Salmon with Mashed Peas

Serves: 1

Cooking Time: 20 minutes

Ingredients and Portions/Measurements:

- Salmon Fillet: 150g (High in omega-3 fatty acids, soft texture suitable for dysphagia diet)
- Olive Oil: 1 teaspoon (For baking, provides healthy fats)
- Fresh Dill: To taste (For flavor, easy to digest)
- Frozen Peas, cooked and mashed: ½ cup (High in vitamins and fiber, mashed to ensure easy swallowing)
- Lemon Juice: 1 tablespoon (For flavor, vitamin C for immune support)

Instructions:

- Preheat your oven to 350°F (175°C).
- Place the salmon fillet on a baking sheet, brush with olive oil, and sprinkle with dill.
- Bake for 15-18 minutes, or until the salmon flakes easily with a fork.

- Meanwhile, cook peas according to package instructions, mash thoroughly, and mix with lemon juice.
- Serve the baked salmon with the mashed peas on the side.

Scientific Notes:

- Salmon Fillet: Rich in omega-3 fatty acids, which are crucial for brain health and reducing inflammation. The soft texture of cooked salmon is perfect for those on a dysphagia diet.
- Olive Oil: Contains healthy monounsaturated fats, beneficial for cardiovascular health.
- Fresh Dill: Aromatic herb that can aid digestion and provide a subtle flavor to the dish without the need for salt.
- Peas: A great source of vitamins A, C, K, and several B vitamins, as well as dietary fiber. Cooking and mashing peas make them safer and easier to swallow for dysphagia patients.
- Lemon Juice: Adds flavor and provides a good amount of vitamin C, essential for repairing tissues and immune function.

Nutritional Information (per serving):

- Calories: Approx. 320
- Protein: 23g
- Total Fat: 15g
- Saturated Fat: Low
- Carbohydrates: 18g
- Sodium: Low

Soft-Cooked Egg with Avocado Toast

Serves: 1

Cooking Time: 10 minutes

Ingredients and Portions/Measurements:

- Egg: 1 large (High in protein, cooked soft for easy swallowing)
- Avocado: ½, mashed (Provides healthy fats, creamy texture suitable for dysphagia diet)
- Soft Whole Grain Bread: 1 slice, toasted lightly (High in fiber, toasted lightly to maintain softness)
- Black Pepper: To taste (For flavor, minimal risk of irritation)

Instructions:

- Boil the egg to your preferred softness, aiming for a soft-boiled texture that's easier to swallow.
- Mash the avocado with a fork and spread it over the lightly toasted bread.
- Peel the soft-boiled egg, slice it, and place it on top of the avocado toast.
- Sprinkle with black pepper to taste and serve immediately.

Scientific Notes:

- Egg: A nutrient-dense food providing high-quality protein and essential vitamins, including B12 and selenium. Soft-cooking ensures it remains easy to swallow.
- Avocado: Rich in monounsaturated fats for heart health. Its creamy texture helps moisten the bread, making it easier to swallow.
- Whole Grain Bread: Provides fiber for digestive health. Light toasting keeps the bread soft enough for individuals with dysphagia.
- Black Pepper: Adds flavor without sodium. The amount used can be adjusted to avoid any potential for irritation or difficulty in swallowing.

Nutritional Information (per serving):

- Calories: Approx. 300
- Protein: 10g
- Total Fat: 20g
- Saturated Fat: Low
- Carbohydrates: 20g
- Sodium: Low

LUNCH RECIPES LEVEL 3
[ADVANCED DIET]

Creamy Butternut Squash Soup

Serves: 1

Cooking Time: 30 minutes

Ingredients and Portions/Measurements:

- Butternut Squash, peeled and cubed: 1 cup (High in vitamins A and C, fiber)
- Vegetable Broth: 1 cup (Base for the soup, low in sodium)
- Onion, finely chopped: ¼ cup (Flavor base, high in antioxidants)
- Garlic, minced: ½ teaspoon (For flavor, antimicrobial properties)
- Ground Nutmeg: A pinch (For flavor, aids in digestion)
- Cream (or Coconut Cream for a dairy-free option): 2 tablespoons (Adds creaminess, helps in achieving a smooth texture)

Instructions:

- In a pot, combine the butternut squash, vegetable broth, onion, and garlic. Bring to a boil, then reduce heat and simmer until the squash is tender, about 20 minutes.
- Remove from heat and let cool slightly. Puree the mixture using a blender until smooth.
- Return the soup to the pot, stir in the nutmeg and cream, and heat through.
- Serve warm.

Scientific Notes:

- Butternut Squash: Rich in beta-carotene, which the body converts to vitamin A, essential for immune function and eye health. Its soft texture post-cooking is ideal for a dysphagia diet.
- Vegetable Broth: Provides a flavorful base without the need for added sodium, which is beneficial for blood pressure management.
- Onion and Garlic: Both are known for their antioxidant and antimicrobial properties, contributing to overall health and adding depth to the soup's flavor.

- Nutmeg: Adds a warm flavor and can aid in digestion. It's important to use it in moderation due to its potent flavor.
- Cream/Coconut Cream: Adds a rich, creamy texture to the soup, making it smoother and easier to swallow for those on a dysphagia diet.

Nutritional Information (per serving):

- Calories: Approx. 200
- Protein: 2g
- Total Fat: 12g
- Saturated Fat: 7g (if using dairy cream)
- Carbohydrates: 22g
- Sodium: Low

Steamed Cod with Sweet Potato Mash

Serves: 1

Cooking Time: 25 minutes

Ingredients and Portions/Measurements:

- Cod Fillet: 150g (High in omega-3 fatty acids, easily digestible protein suitable for dysphagia diet)
- Sweet Potato, peeled and cubed: ½ cup (Rich in beta-carotene and fiber, softened and mashed for ease of swallowing)
- Olive Oil: 1 teaspoon (For mashing with sweet potato, adds healthy fats)
- Parsley, finely chopped: To taste (For garnish and flavor, optional for those sensitive to certain herbs)
- Lemon Wedge: For serving (Provides vitamin C and enhances flavor without salt)

Instructions:

- Steam the cod fillet for 15-20 minutes or until it flakes easily with a fork. Ensure it's thoroughly cooked to maintain softness suitable for dysphagia.
- Boil sweet potato cubes until soft, then drain and mash with olive oil until smooth.

- Serve the steamed cod over the sweet potato mash, garnished with parsley (if using) and a squeeze of lemon juice.

Scientific Notes:

- Cod Fillet: Provides a high-quality protein source that's low in fat. The gentle cooking process retains moisture, making it easier to swallow.
- Sweet Potato: A good source of complex carbohydrates, beta-carotene (converted to vitamin A in the body), and fiber. Mashing increases its palatability and ease of swallowing.
- Olive Oil: Rich in monounsaturated fats, beneficial for heart health. Adds moisture to the sweet potato mash, aiding in swallowing.
- Parsley: Offers a mild diuretic effect and is rich in vitamins K, C, and A. It's optional due to potential sensitivities but can enhance flavor and nutritional content.
- Lemon: The acidity can help stimulate saliva production, making swallowing easier, and provides a vitamin C boost.

Nutritional Information (per serving):

- Calories: Approx. 300
- Protein: 22g
- Total Fat: 10g
- Saturated Fat: Low
- Carbohydrates: 28g
- Sodium: Low

Pulled Chicken over Creamy Polenta

Serves: 1

Cooking Time: 30 minutes

Ingredients and Portions/Measurements:

- Chicken Breast: 150g (Poached and pulled, high in protein, soft texture)
- Cornmeal (for Polenta): ¼ cup (Provides carbohydrates, smooth texture when cooked)
- Chicken Broth: 1 cup (Used for cooking polenta, adds flavor, low sodium)
- Parmesan Cheese, grated: 1 tablespoon (Adds flavor and calcium, optional for those with dairy sensitivities)
- Spinach, steamed and chopped: ¼ cup (High in iron and vitamins, ensures easy swallowing when finely chopped)

Instructions:

- Poach the chicken breast until fully cooked, then pull apart using forks to create a soft, shredded texture.
- Cook cornmeal in chicken broth according to package instructions until it forms a creamy polenta.

- Stir in parmesan cheese into the polenta once cooked for added flavor (omit if dairy-sensitive).
- Serve the pulled chicken over the creamy polenta, topped with steamed and chopped spinach.

Scientific Notes:

- Chicken Breast: An excellent source of lean protein, aiding in muscle repair. Cooking by poaching ensures tenderness, making it easier to swallow.
- Cornmeal: The basis for polenta, which is gluten-free and provides energy through carbohydrates. Its creamy texture is ideal for dysphagia diets.
- Chicken Broth: Adds nutrients and flavor to the polenta, ensuring the meal is moist and easier to swallow.
- Parmesan Cheese: Provides calcium for bone health. It can be omitted for those who are dairy intolerant or sensitive to dairy products.
- Spinach: Rich in vitamins A, C, K, iron, and folate. Steaming and chopping make it easier to consume and digest.

Nutritional Information (per serving):

- Calories: Approx. 350

- Protein: 28g
- Total Fat: 12g
- Saturated Fat: Low
- Carbohydrates: 30g
- Sodium: Moderate

Soft Lentil Patties with Yogurt Sauce

Serves: 1

Cooking Time: 30 minutes

Ingredients and Portions/Measurements:

- Cooked Lentils: ½ cup (High in protein and fiber, mashed for smooth texture)
- Egg: 1 (Binds the patties, adds protein, cook thoroughly to ensure softness)
- Bread Crumbs: 2 tablespoons (Gluten-free if necessary, helps bind the patties)
- Cumin Powder: ¼ teaspoon (For flavor, aids digestion)
- Greek Yogurt: ¼ cup (For sauce, provides calcium and probiotics, use dairy-free alternative if necessary)
- Fresh Mint, finely chopped: 1 tablespoon (For mixing into yogurt, optional for flavor and digestive benefits)

Instructions:

- Mix mashed lentils, beaten egg, bread crumbs, and cumin powder to form a soft mixture.
- Form into small patties and cook in a lightly oiled pan over medium heat until each side is golden brown, ensuring they remain soft and moist inside.
- Mix Greek yogurt with chopped mint for the sauce.
- Serve the lentil patties with a dollop of mint yogurt sauce on the side.

Scientific Notes:

- Lentils: A great source of plant-based protein and fiber, supporting digestive health. Mashing lentils helps achieve a texture that's easier to swallow.
- Egg: Provides high-quality protein and various vitamins. Cooking the egg within the patties ensures they are soft and moist.
- Bread Crumbs: Helps bind the patties together, making them easier to handle and chew. Choose gluten-free options if necessary for dietary restrictions.
- Cumin: Known for its digestive benefits and adds a warm, earthy flavor to the patties.

- Greek Yogurt: A good source of calcium and probiotics, which support bone health and digestive wellness. A dairy-free alternative can be used for those with sensitivities.
- Mint: Can aid digestion and adds a fresh flavor to the yogurt sauce. It's optional and can be omitted based on preference or dietary restrictions.

Nutritional Information (per serving):

- Calories: Approx. 400
- Protein: 24g
- Total Fat: 12g
- Saturated Fat: Low
- Carbohydrates: 44g
- Sodium: Low

Gentle Beef Stew

Serves: 1

Cooking Time: 2 hours

Ingredients and Portions/Measurements:

- Beef Chuck, cut into small pieces: 150g (Rich in protein, cooked until very tender)
- Carrots, peeled and sliced: ¼ cup (Softened in the stew, high in vitamin A)
- Potatoes, peeled and cubed: ¼ cup (Provides carbohydrates, softened for ease of swallowing)
- Low Sodium Beef Broth: 1 cup (Adds flavor, keeps the stew moist)
- Thyme: ½ teaspoon (For flavor, easy to digest)
- (Substitution) Olive Oil: 1 teaspoon (For browning beef, adds healthy fats)

Instructions:

- In a pot, heat olive oil over medium heat and brown the beef chunks lightly on all sides.
- Add the carrots, potatoes, beef broth, and thyme. Bring to a boil.

- Reduce heat to low, cover, and simmer for about 2 hours, or until the beef and vegetables are very tender.
- Break the beef and vegetables down further with a fork if necessary to ensure they are easy to swallow.

Scientific Notes:

- Beef Chuck: Provides essential proteins for muscle repair and maintenance. Long cooking times ensure the meat is tender enough for those on a dysphagia diet.
- Carrots and Potatoes: Both vegetables are high in vitamins and minerals. Cooking until very soft ensures they are easy to swallow and digest.
- Low Sodium Beef Broth: Keeps the dish moist, aiding in swallowing, while controlling sodium intake to manage blood pressure.
- Olive Oil: A source of monounsaturated fats, beneficial for heart health.

Nutritional Information (per serving):

- Calories: Approx. 350
- Protein: 28g
- Total Fat: 15g

DINNER RECIPES LEVEL 3
[ADVANCED DIET]

Fluffy Ricotta Pancakes

Serves: 1

Cooking Time: 20 minutes

Ingredients and Portions/Measurements:

- Ricotta Cheese: ¼ cup (Provides calcium and protein, soft texture)
- Egg: 1 (Adds structure and protein, ensure well-cooked)
- Gluten-Free Flour: 2 tablespoons (For those with gluten intolerance, provides carbohydrates)
- Vanilla Extract: ¼ teaspoon (For flavor)
- (Substitution) Maple Syrup: 1 tablespoon (For serving, natural sweetener)

Instructions:

- In a bowl, mix together the ricotta cheese, egg, gluten-free flour, and vanilla extract until smooth.
- Heat a non-stick pan over medium heat and pour in batter to form small pancakes.

- Cook until bubbles form on the surface, then flip and cook until golden brown.
- Serve warm with maple syrup.

Scientific Notes:

- Ricotta Cheese: High in protein and calcium, which are essential for bone health and muscle function. Its soft texture is ideal for a dysphagia diet.
- Egg: Provides high-quality protein and vitamins. Cooking thoroughly ensures it's safe and soft for swallowing.
- Gluten-Free Flour: Makes this recipe suitable for those with gluten sensitivities, providing a source of carbohydrates for energy.
- Maple Syrup: A natural sweetener, easier on the digestive system than refined sugars.

Nutritional Information (per serving):

- Calories: Approx. 300
- Protein: 14g
- Total Fat: 16g
- Saturated Fat: Low
- Carbohydrates: 22g
- Sodium: Moderate

Silky Pumpkin Soup

Serves: 1

Cooking Time: 45 minutes

Ingredients and Portions/Measurements:

- Pumpkin, peeled and cubed: 1 cup (High in vitamins, cooked until soft)
- Low Sodium Vegetable Broth: 1 cup (Base for the soup, adds flavor without excess sodium)
- Onion, minced: 2 tablespoons (Flavor base, softened during cooking)
- Garlic, minced: ½ teaspoon (For flavor, antimicrobial properties)
- (Substitution) Coconut Milk: 2 tablespoons (For creaminess, dairy-free option)

Instructions:

- In a pot, combine pumpkin, vegetable broth, onion, and garlic. Bring to a boil.
- Reduce heat to low and simmer until the pumpkin is very soft, about 30 minutes.
- Puree the mixture using a blender until smooth.

- Return to the pot, stir in coconut milk, and warm through before serving.

Scientific Notes:

- Pumpkin: A good source of beta-carotene, which converts to vitamin A in the body, supporting vision and immune health. Soft texture after cooking is crucial for ease of swallowing.
- Low Sodium Vegetable Broth: Helps maintain hydration and adds flavor without the risk of increasing blood pressure.
- Coconut Milk: Provides a creamy texture without dairy, suitable for those with lactose intolerance or dairy sensitivities.

Nutritional Information (per serving):

- Calories: Approx. 200
- Protein: 3g
- Total Fat: 9g
- Saturated Fat: 7g (from coconut milk)
- Carbohydrates: 28g
- Sodium: Low

Soft Pear and Cottage Cheese Salad

Serves: 1

Cooking Time: No cooking required

Ingredients and Portions/Measurements:

- Ripe Pear, peeled and finely diced: ½ pear (Soft texture, high in fiber)
- Cottage Cheese: ½ cup (Provides protein, soft and easy to swallow)
- Honey: 1 tablespoon (Natural sweetener, easier on the digestive system than refined sugar)
- Cinnamon: A pinch (For flavor, aids in digestion)
- (Substitution for Pear) Baked Apple: ½ apple, if pear is not tolerated (Soft texture, high in fiber)

Instructions:

- In a small bowl, combine the finely diced pear (or baked apple if substituting) with cottage cheese.
- Drizzle honey over the top and sprinkle with a pinch of cinnamon.
- Gently mix to combine all ingredients.

Scientific Notes:

- Pear: Soft when ripe and high in fiber, which aids in digestion. Pears are also rich in vitamins C and K.
- Cottage Cheese: A good source of calcium and protein, important for bone and muscle health. The soft texture is suitable for those on a dysphagia diet.
- Honey: Provides a natural source of sweetness and has antibacterial properties. It's also easier to digest than refined sugars.
- Cinnamon: Known for its anti-inflammatory properties and can help regulate blood sugar levels.

Nutritional Information (per serving):

- Calories: Approx. 200
- Protein: 14g
- Total Fat: 2g
- Saturated Fat: Low
- Carbohydrates: 35g
- Sodium: Moderate

Smooth Carrot Soup with Ginger

Serves: 1

Cooking Time: 25 minutes

Ingredients and Portions/Measurements:

- Carrots, peeled and chopped: 1 cup (Softens when cooked, high in beta-carotene)
- Low Sodium Vegetable Broth: 1 cup (Adds flavor without excess sodium)
- Ginger, minced: ½ teaspoon (Aids digestion, adds flavor)
- Olive Oil: 1 teaspoon (For sautéing ginger, adds healthy fats)
- (Substitution for Ginger) Ground Fennel: ¼ teaspoon, if ginger is not tolerated (Aids digestion, adds a mild flavor)

Instructions:

- In a pot, heat olive oil over medium heat and sauté ginger (or ground fennel if substituting) for 1 minute.
- Add the chopped carrots and vegetable broth. Bring to a boil, then simmer until the carrots are very soft, about 20 minutes.

- Puree the soup in a blender until smooth.
- Serve warm.

Scientific Notes:

- Carrots: High in beta-carotene, which the body converts to vitamin A, essential for vision and immune function. Cooking and blending make them easier to swallow.
- Ginger: Stimulates digestion and adds a warming flavor. It's also known for its anti-inflammatory effects.
- Olive Oil: A source of monounsaturated fats, beneficial for heart health.

Nutritional Information (per serving):

- Calories: Approx. 150
- Protein: 2g
- Total Fat: 5g
- Saturated Fat: Low
- Carbohydrates: 24g
- Sodium: Low

Tender Turkey Meatballs in Tomato Sauce

Serves: 1

Cooking Time: 30 minutes

Ingredients and Portions/Measurements:

- Ground Turkey: 100g (High in protein, cooked until very tender)
- Bread Crumbs: 1 tablespoon (Helps bind the meatballs, choose gluten-free if necessary)
- Egg: ¼ beaten (For binding, adds protein)
- Tomato Sauce, low sodium: ½ cup (Adds flavor, vitamin C)
- Basil: ½ teaspoon (For flavor, anti-inflammatory properties)
- (Substitution for Ground Turkey) Ground Chicken: 100g, if turkey is not tolerated (High in protein, similarly tender when cooked)

Instructions:

- Preheat the oven to 375°F (190°C).
- Mix ground turkey (or ground chicken if substituting), bread crumbs, beaten egg, and basil in a bowl.

- Form into small meatballs and place on a baking sheet.
- Bake for 20-25 minutes, or until cooked through.
- Warm the tomato sauce in a pan and add the cooked meatballs. Simmer for 5 minutes to infuse the flavor.
- Serve the meatballs with sauce.

Scientific Notes:

- Ground Turkey/Chicken: Lean sources of protein important for muscle maintenance and repair. Cooking thoroughly ensures tenderness suitable for dysphagia diets.
- Tomato Sauce: Rich in lycopene, an antioxidant that may reduce the risk of certain diseases. Using low sodium sauce helps manage blood pressure.
- Basil: Adds flavor without the need for salt and has anti-inflammatory and antibacterial properties.

Nutritional Information (per serving):

- Calories: Approx. 300
- Protein: 22g
- Total Fat: 16g
- Saturated Fat: Low

7 DAYS MEAL PLAN FOR PHASE 3

Day 1

Breakfast: Quinoa Porridge with Almond Milk

Lunch: Creamy Butternut Squash Soup

Dinner: Silky Pumpkin Soup

Day 2

Breakfast: Creamy Carrot and Ginger Soup

Lunch: Steamed Cod with Sweet Potato Mash

Dinner: Tender Turkey Meatballs in Tomato Sauce

Day 3

Breakfast: Soft-Cooked Egg with Avocado Toast

Lunch: Pulled Chicken over Creamy Polenta

Dinner: Fluffy Ricotta Pancakes

Day 4

Breakfast: Creamy Avocado and Spinach Pasta

Lunch: Soft Lentil Patties with Yogurt Sauce

Dinner: Smooth Carrot Soup with Ginger

Day 5

Breakfast: Tender Salmon with Mashed Peas

Lunch: Gentle Beef Stew

Dinner: Soft Pear and Cottage Cheese Salad

Day 6

Breakfast: Creamy Carrot and Ginger Soup

Lunch: Creamy Butternut Squash Soup

Dinner: Tender Turkey Meatballs in Tomato Sauce

Day 7

Breakfast: Quinoa Porridge with Almond Milk

Lunch: Steamed Cod with Sweet Potato Mash

Dinner: Fluffy Ricotta Pancakes

7 DAYS MEAL PLANNER

NEGLECT THE SNACKS AND APPETIZER

AMOS JIMMY
DAILY MEAL PLANNER

DATE _____   M T W T F S S
:

BREAKFAST

DINNER

LUNCH

NOTES

SNACKS

JIMMY'S CULINARY HAVEN

Jimmy Asking For An Honest Review

I wanted to reach out and personally thank you for taking the time to explore the world of flavors and creations that I poured into those pages.

Your experience matters a lot to me, and I would be truly grateful if you could share your honest thoughts in a review. Whether it's a brief note or a detailed reflection, your feedback will not only help me grow as a creator but also guide fellow food enthusiasts in deciding if this cookbook is a culinary adventure they'd like to embark on.

Feel free to highlight your favorite recipes, share any challenges you conquered, or even suggest what you'd love to see more of in future editions. Your unique perspective adds a special spice to the whole mix!

Thank you again for being a part of this delicious

Made in the USA
Las Vegas, NV
08 August 2024